Contents Contents Contents

Contents Contents

Special Features

Features

Carving Up the Earth

Written by Ned Jensen

Many forces are at work changing the Earth. Some of these forces are constantly changing the face of the Earth.

Sometimes these forces work quickly and the changes are easy to see, for example, landslides. At other times the forces work very slowly. In fact, these forces work so slowly that it takes hundreds of thousands, or even millions of years for them to make changes you can see.

A river cutting a canyon is an example of a slow change. It takes millions of years for a river to form a canyon.

The natural forces that are constantly working to change the face of the Earth include weather-related forces such as wind and rain. Other forces include rivers, waves, glaciers, deep movements below the surface, and human activity.

Effects of Running Water

Running water in streams and rivers is one of nature's most powerful agents of change. The force of fast-moving water cuts canyons, like the Grand Canyon in Arizona. The water carries large rocks and sand. As the rocks and sand move past rough surfaces, the rock is broken up into smaller pieces. The water then carries away the smaller pieces. The tumbling action of the rocks makes even smaller rocks. After millions of years, the water carves deep canyons into the face of the Earth.

Slow-moving water can also wear away the land. Slow-moving rivers form large valleys, rather than steep canyons.

It takes millions of years for a river to form a canyon.

Moving water does not just carve away at the Earth. It also deposits land. Deltas are examples of land formations made by water leaving deposits behind. The deposits form when rivers slow down as they enter the sea or large lakes. When a river slows, particles carried by the water settle and begin to build up. Huge deltas can be found at the mouths of large rivers such as the Nile in Egypt, the Ganges in India, and the Mississippi in the United States.

Water that falls from clouds begins its work as soon as it strikes the Earth. As the water runs over the surface, it picks up small particles of sand and dirt. The faster the water moves, the more it can change the Earth. This action of water is called erosion.

Deltas are examples of land formations made by water leaving deposits behind.

Tongariro River Delta, New Zealand

Effects of Waves

Along coastal areas, you can see the work of waves. As waves constantly pound the shore, they break up the rock into smaller rocks. The smaller rocks eventually break up into sand. These changes usually occur slowly. But during fierce coastal storms, changes can occur rapidly.

Waves and currents are constantly changing the look of the shoreline. Depending on wave size, direction, and currents, sand can be either deposited or removed. This action changes the look of a beach. Cliffs along the shore are eventually worn down by waves pounding against them. The wave action can also form caves in cliffs, arches, and other formations such as sea stacks. Softer rock wears away first. This leaves the harder rock behind. The sea often carves this rock into interesting shapes.

Waves make a big impact on the shape of the coastline.

Effects of Frozen Water

Major changes on the Earth's surface are caused by frozen water moving slowly in the form of glaciers.

During the Ice Age, large sections of North America were covered with ice. These very thick sheets of ice acted like giant bulldozers. They carved out wide valleys. The soil in front of the glaciers was crumpled up as if it were carpet being pushed along. As a result, when the glaciers receded, hills and valleys were left behind. These glaciers are known as continental glaciers. Today, continental glaciers cover Greenland and Antarctica.

Alpine glaciers are found in mountain ranges throughout the world. They form in areas where there is more snow falling than there is ice melting. As the snow builds up over the years, it forms large, slow-moving glaciers.

Glaciers create major changes on the Earth's surface.

Effects of Wind

Wind blowing over barren land picks up sand and dirt. It leaves behind land covered by pebbles and large stones. The sand carried by the wind carves up the surrounding land. Some interesting land formations can be formed by the wind. The Badlands of South Dakota in the United States is an example of an area carved by wind erosion.

When the wind slows down, the particles it carries are deposited. You can often find large deposits called sand dunes in areas near the sea, large inland lakes, and deserts. The wind is strong and usually blows from one direction in areas where dunes form. Dunes in the deserts of North Africa and Saudi Arabia are very large and stretch out over great distances.

When the wind deposits dirt instead of sand, loess is formed. Loess is a fine-grained, yellowish-brown soil, that is good for growing crops.

You can often find large deposits called sand dunes in areas near the sea, large inland lakes, and deserts.

Effects of Deep Forces

Not all the changes to the Earth's surface are caused by forces on the surface. Some of the most spectacular formations come from forces deep beneath the Earth.

The Earth's crust is made up of giant plates. These plates are slowly moving. In some areas, they are moving into each other. In other areas, they are moving apart. In yet other areas, they are moving alongside each other. When one plate moves under another plate, large mountains form along the boundary. The Himalayan mountains in Asia have formed along the boundary of two colliding plates. The mountains continue to grow as the plates continue to move.

The movement of plates also results in earthquakes and erupting volcanoes. They both cause changes to the Earth's surface. Earthquakes cause landslides. Volcanic eruptions can build mountains and destroy them. Mount Kilimanjaro, in Tanzania, is a large volcanic mountain.

The movement of plates also results in earthquakes and erupting volcanoes.

Logging often causes erosion.

Effects of Humans

Nature is not the only force working to change the Earth. Humans can also have a great effect on the look of the Earth's surface.

Clearing trees from steep hillsides and mountains can result in severe erosion. In areas where people have removed all the trees and low-growing vegetation to make farmland, the soil is exposed. That makes it easier for wind and water to pick up the loose soil and sand and carry it away. Overgrazing of these grasslands can easily turn these lands into deserts.

Removal of minerals from the land in a process called strip mining has also left large scars on the Earth's surface. Coal, copper, and iron ore are examples of minerals removed through surface or strip mining. In some regions, highway and building construction and the building of dams have altered the face of the Earth dramatically.

Safari POWER

Word Meanings

atolls
a — mountains
b — big land masses
c — coral islands

barren
a — bare
b — small
c — with many plants

campaign
a — plan of action
b — banner
c — report

compacted
a — wide
b — tightly packed
c — quickly opened

exceedingly
a — hardly
b — extremely
c — often

igneous
a — of intense heat
b — of intense cold
c — jagged

imperceptibly
a — noisily
b — very obviously
c — unnoticeably

motionless
a — still
b — moving
c — climbing

overgrazing
a — graze too much
b — without grazing
c — overlooking

receded
a — pushed ahead
b — withdrew
c — grew

reclusive
a — hidden away
b — very loud
c — knowledgeable

spectacular
a — big
b — dull
c — amazing

Answers on page 21

Rock Cycle

Written by Tracey Reeder

Magma.
Molten material
Melting deep within the Earth,
Pressured from above.

Crystallization.
Intrusive igneous rock
In the Earth's crust,
Extrusive igneous rock
On the Earth's surface.

Weathering.
Water, wind, rain, ice,
Transports, deposits sediments,
Buried, compacted
Sedimentary rock.

Metamorphism.
Temperature, pressure, fluids,
Minerals,
Metamorphic rocks.

Magma.

Friends of SANDY BAY

Written by Ruby Maile • Illustrated by Mark Wilson

You might think that city kids would get bored spending every holiday weekend in a small town like Sandy Bay, but Pat and I loved staying with Auntie Bev and Uncle Joe. Auntie Bev is my mother's twin sister and my brother and I are like the children she didn't have. This holiday weekend was no exception and we were both full of anticipation as we got on the bus.

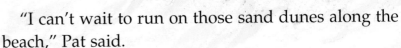

"I can't wait to run on those sand dunes along the beach," Pat said.

"What do you mean, run on the sand dunes?" I asked. "I thought we'd agreed not to do that again after that woman came and spoke to us at school."

"Why she came to talk to city kids, I'll never know," Pat replied. "And anyway, she wasn't talking about the dunes at Sandy Bay. She meant really big sand dunes in other places."

"No, she didn't mean other dunes," I reminded him. "When she talked about sand dunes and how people walking and playing in them was one of the causes of erosion, she meant all sand dunes, even the ones at Sandy Bay."

Pat obviously didn't want to argue, so the subject was dropped, and we mostly dozed until we reached the Brockbee bus station very late that night. Uncle Joe and Auntie Bev were there to meet us. The car ride was full of talk about how everyone was and how things might have changed, but we would have to wait until the morning to see for ourselves.

I was up early the next morning even though I was tired. I never slept well my first night away from home. I headed for the beach, wanting to view the sun rising over the dunes, but within minutes I was back inside the house. By now my uncle was in the kitchen and after quickly hugging him good morning, I asked him, "What happened to the sand dunes?"

"Erosion," he replied. "It's an issue that's dividing Sandy Bay right now. Some of the townsfolk want to do something about it, but others just don't care. And no one has taken a leadership role for either side."

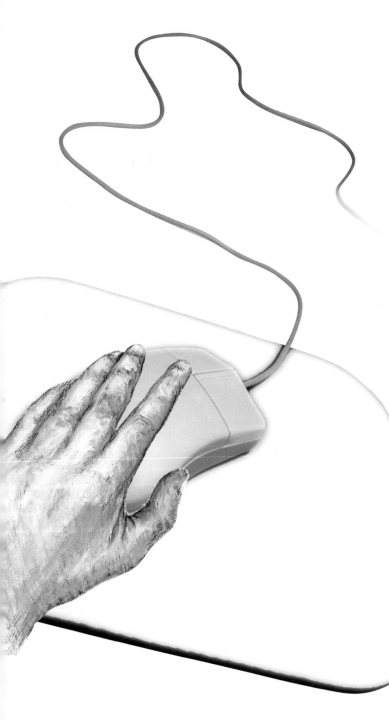

"The dunes look absolutely terrible, and ecosystems are being destroyed," said my aunt, coming into the room.

"You sound like the woman who came to our school," I said, hugging her. "But surely there must be something we can do," I added.

Already ideas were forming in my head. You see, I like to get involved with things like this and I was certain that before we left Sandy Bay I would have organized something. I knew that Pat certainly wouldn't be interested in spending his weekend helping, so I'd have to do it on my own or think of a way of persuading him. Maybe my aunt and uncle would help.

"I think we need to get together some sort of group to work on saving the dunes from further destruction," I said in between bites of warm pancakes that my uncle was cooking.

"That's a good idea," he replied, "but we know so little about it."

"Maybe we could find some more information on the Internet," I said. "Let me do that and then we can talk about what to do next."

I spent the rest of the morning finding out information about how to save sand dunes, while Pat lazed on the beach.

During lunch, Auntie Bev suddenly said, "You should go and talk to Jock. He's really into this sort of thing."

"What do you think Jock can do?" I asked, remembering a reclusive sort of person with a bad limp, not much older than Pat and I.

"I think you might be surprised," Uncle Joe said.

"I don't want to spend my weekend saving the world," Pat said, predictably. "Is it all right if I go up to the farm and visit Ned?"

"As long as you're back by five o'clock," Auntie Bev told him. "Amy and I will go and see Jock."

Jock was a strange sort of person who you could easily mistake for someone who's slow to catch on to things. He took a long time to respond to anything I said, but as I talked to him about the dunes, I realized that appearances could be exceedingly deceptive and that he was actually extremely knowledgeable.

"I'm glad some city folk are concerned about the environment," he said in his slow, sleepy drawl. "If you can come up with a plan you can count me in."

As it turned out, he didn't really mean that at all. In no time, he was making all the suggestions and I was making notes in case I forgot some of his pearls of wisdom.

"First, we need a strategy," Jock said. "What is it we want to achieve and how are we going to do it? When we decide that, we should call a meeting. Our plan should be to turn everyone around to our way of thinking, but let them think that they came up with the ideas themselves."

"How do we do that?" I asked.

"Well, I guess we've already sorted out that we want to protect the remaining sand dunes. Now we just have to sort out how," Jock said.

"I read on the Internet about replanting native grasses," I said.

"That's a good idea," Jock commented. "Did you find out anything else?"

"We could build some fences to cut down the force of the wind and trap the wind-blown sand," I said. "That's been successful in some areas."

"Anything else?" Jock asked, although I had the feeling he knew all this already.

"What about signs asking people to keep off the sand dunes and explaining why?" I replied. "Fenced off walkways to and from the beach might help."

"Those are all good ideas," said Jock, again nodding appreciatively. "Now we just have to sell the reasons for protecting the sand dunes to those people in the community who couldn't care less."

"We could make flyers to put into everyone's mailboxes to let them know what we're doing," suggested my aunt. "Then we could invite them to a meeting to find out more information. I'm sure people will make more suggestions at the meeting, too."

"We're going to need a lot of help from people if we want to do all these things," said Jock. "Let's get those flyers done first. Maybe we could start working on them tonight."

"Join us for dinner," said my aunt.

But it wasn't to be.

When we got home, we found a note from my uncle to say that there had been an accident up at the farm and that Pat had been hurt. He was at the hospital and my parents were on their way. Auntie Bev telephoned Jock to tell him of the changed plans, then she and I drove to the hospital, our hearts in our mouths.

Supposedly Pat and Ned had been fooling around on an old disused farm truck, when, for some unknown reason, its brakes had failed. It careened down a bank, landing on its side, and was stopped by a wire fence. Pat had sustained back and leg injuries. As we fearfully waited for a doctor to explain the situation more fully to us, my parents arrived. I could tell that my mother had been crying and my father looked suddenly years older than he had yesterday. After endless hours at the hospital we learned that Pat had indeed broken his back, but there was no permanent damage. Surgery, physical therapy, and time would eventually see him back to normal. The burning question was how to deal with the present. My parents ran their own business in the city and couldn't just shut the doors. In the end, Auntie Bev persuaded them to let both of us stay until Pat could be safely moved back home.

After the drama of Pat's accident had passed and my parents had returned home, I turned my mind back to the sand dune issue.

I went to see Jock and between us we designed the flyer and got it copied at the local library.

"You'll have to run the meeting yourself," Jock said. "I'm no good at public speaking."

"Neither am I," I thought to myself, but I certainly had more confidence than Jock.

I wrote down what I wanted to say and rehearsed it over and over again until I knew it by heart.

Jock and I were both very nervous as the hall filled with local people, some friendly, some not so friendly. When everyone had settled down, Auntie Bev introduced me.

Jock smiled encouragingly from the back row as I stood up to speak, but even his smile couldn't calm the butterflies flying around in my stomach. I fixed my eyes on a kind-looking woman in the middle of the sea of faces and began. It was nerve-wracking at first, but it got better as I went along. Occasionally I caught sight of Jock's head nodding in agreement as I spoke and that gave me more confidence.

Save the sand dunes of Sandy Bay!
Meet to discuss proposals Wednesday 7 o'clock, local hall

When I'd finished, people began to talk amongst themselves. The mood was generally supportive, except for a few four-wheel drive enthusiasts who wanted to drive all over the sand dunes, and some surfers who didn't want to be told where they could access the beach. One man and woman were adamant that they didn't want to be part of any campaign to save the sand dunes, as they wanted to bulldoze some of the dunes directly in front of their house to improve their ocean view.

It was decided to take a vote. Jock and I were delighted when the majority voted to protect the sand dunes. And so that night, a group called Friends of Sandy Bay was formed.

Safari POINT OF VIEW

I don't think that the group, Friends of Sandy Bay, should have been formed. I think that girl Amy should have minded her own business. It didn't matter that the sand dunes were being flattened. Sand dunes are difficult to get across when you want to get onto the beach and they're ugly, too.

Also, if the sand dunes disappeared, some people would have great views of the ocean. I know I'd rather look at the sea than at lumps of sand. Why did Amy feel so strongly about it, anyway? Her brother had the right idea. He just wanted to enjoy his vacation and not worry about anything. But she couldn't help interfering, could she?

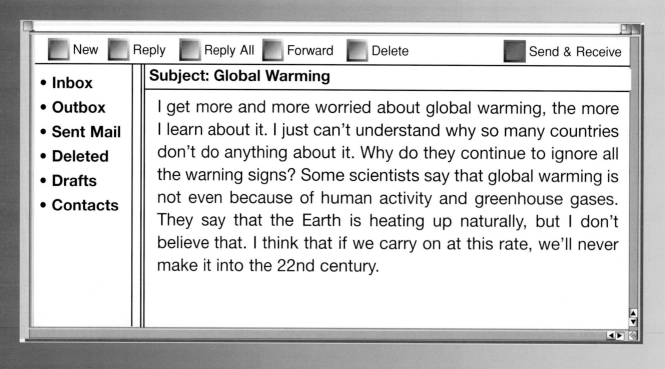

| New | Reply | Reply All | Forward | Delete | Send & Receive |

- **Inbox**
- **Outbox**
- **Sent Mail**
- **Deleted**
- **Drafts**
- **Contacts**

Subject: Global Warming

I get more and more worried about global warming, the more I learn about it. I just can't understand why so many countries don't do anything about it. Why do they continue to ignore all the warning signs? Some scientists say that global warming is not even because of human activity and greenhouse gases. They say that the Earth is heating up naturally, but I don't believe that. I think that if we carry on at this rate, we'll never make it into the 22nd century.

Safari POWER

atolls
c – coral islands

imperceptibly
c – unnoticeably

barren
a – bare

motionless
a – still

campaign
a – plan of action

overgrazing
a – graze too much

compacted
b – tightly packed

receded
b – withdrew

exceedingly
b – extremely

reclusive
a – hidden away

igneous
a – of intense heat

spectacular
c – amazing

a
b
c

Xtra for Xperts

What is a boundary?

Rating Scale

10-12 Excellent   7-9 Very good   4-6 Good   0-3 Try again

A Future History Lesson

Written by Bill Francis

Characters

Abdul **Ali** **Ibrahim** **Miriam** **Narrator** **Thobeela**

Setting

The year is 2700.

Scene 1

Narrator
Five friends are sitting at a table talking to each other. They are looking at the water far below them.

Thobeela
It sure seems funny living way up here with the city sitting on poles and the water far below.

Ibrahim
Yeah. I often wonder what it must have been like before the water began to rise – when our ancestors lived on the land and the water surrounded them.

Abdul
I guess it would have been very different. What caused the sea to rise and flood the atolls anyway?

Ibrahim
I'm not too sure.

Miriam
I've heard my mother talk about it a lot. She said it was caused by something called global warming.

Abdul
I overheard my parents talking about it as well but I didn't really understand what it was about.

Thobeela
Global warming was all about the Earth heating up and the effects that came about from that – things like the water rising because the polar ice caps melted and the climate changed around the world.

Ali
You seem to know a lot about it.

Thobeela
I went down to the Virtual Deck the other day with my dad. We went right back to the time when our ancestors lived on the atolls. It was a really good thing to do because I learned a lot about our history.

Ibrahim
I've never been there before but it sounds like it would be fun and a much better way to learn about our history than sitting in a classroom reading about it.

Ali

Do you think your dad would be able to book us a time?

Thobeela

I think it would be all right. He did say to let him know if I wanted to go again. Let me talk to him and then I'll send a message to your watch phones with the time to be there. Is everyone interested?

Miriam

I am.

Abdul

Count me in.

Ibrahim

Sure. It would be good to finally get to see what this global warming is all about.

Thobeela

I'll see you all tomorrow, then.

Scene 2

Narrator

The next day, they are all on the Virtual Deck.

Thobeela

During this tour we'll be going back in time. We will all become our ancestors during the tour.

Abdul

How weird.

Thobeela

I know. But I've done it before and you get used to it.

Ali

What do we have to do?

Thobeela

All these machines have been preset with the time, place, and events we wish to participate in. All we have to do is hook up to them and away we go.

Miriam

What time have the machines been preset to?

Thobeela

I thought it would be good to go back to the time when our ancestors held a great meeting to decide what to do about the rising water. We can go back just before the meeting and return just after it. Is that OK with everyone?

Miriam
Sounds good to me.

Abdul
Same with me.

Ibrahim
Will we know when we are on the tour that that is what we are doing?

Thobeela
No. To make this virtual trip more realistic we will just be our ancestors participating in everyday life like all the other people. OK, let's hook up and away we go.

Scene 3

Narrator
The group is sitting on one of the atolls. They have returned as some of their ancestors. The year is 2110.

Thobeela
You know that everyone is talking about the rising water and the weather becoming hotter, but no one is doing anything about it.

Ibrahim
You're right. Just the other week all the inhabitants from Sailfish atoll had to quickly pack up and move over to Wahoo atoll because the rising water flooded their atoll.

Abdul
The funny thing is that they all left it until the very last minute before they moved.

Miriam
I know what you mean. I thought they would have planned a move earlier. But I talked to my friend from over there. She said that many of the elders did not want to go. They said that all their memories were there and they would rather not leave.

Ibrahim
I don't really understand this global warming and what causes it, but I guess that doesn't matter. What matters is that we need to do something or our children and their children will not have a place to grow up in.

Thobeela
I agree, but what can we do?

Abdul

We are the highest atoll but we don't have enough land area to support all the people from the other atolls. And what happens when the water rises high enough to flood us?

Thobeela

We should call a meeting of all the chiefs of all the atolls and try to come up with a plan.

Abdul

That sounds like a good idea. Let's spread the word.

Scene 4

Narrator

The next day, all the chiefs have gathered to talk about the problem.

Thobeela

We have called everyone together to try to come up with a solution to the gradual flooding of the atolls, as the water rises due to global warming.

Ali

What is this global warming? I think it might not be as dangerous as it all sounds.

Miriam

What do you mean "not dangerous"? We've just had to evacuate our atoll because the water has flooded it. If that's not dangerous, I don't know what is.

Thobeela

Global warming is caused by something scientists call the greenhouse effect. Simplified, the Earth is surrounded by gases; some of these gases, including carbon dioxide and methane, are called greenhouse gases. It's the build-up of these gases that leads to global warming. Greenhouse gases trap warm air, keeping the Earth warm. Once the gases themselves are warmed, they radiate some of the heat back to the Earth, creating more warming.

Abdul

Wow. How does this make the sea level rise?

Thobeela

In two ways. First, extra water is produced when the polar ice caps melt. Second, sea water expands as it becomes warmer.

Ibrahim
Is there anything we can do to slow this down or prevent it happening?

Thobeela
There are some things, but people all around the world would have to do them. People could decrease the use of cars, recycle, and reduce rubbish. They could also use less fossil fuels like coal and diesel.

Miriam
Perhaps we could try some of those, but I think at this late stage we need to concentrate more on what we are going to do to save our people. Perhaps we could just move everyone and everything to a new place and then work on trying to prevent global warming.

Ibrahim
What if we built some kind of structures above the ground? Perhaps on poles so we could still use the water for fishing?

Ali
That sounds like a lot of work. Where are we going to get all the timber to use for the poles? How are we going to get the poles to stand in the coral?

Thobeela
We could ask the people of Long Pine Island if we could use some of their wood. But we would need to help them replant anything we used and only take as much as we really need.

Ali
Why don't we all just move to Long Pine Island?

Abdul
Even though the island is large and fairly high above the sea level, there wouldn't be enough room for all of us and the people of Long Pine Island to live there together.

Ali
There goes that idea, then.

Ibrahim
I remember my grandmother talking about a way to make coral grow faster. It was something passed on to her from her mother. Perhaps once the poles are all in place we could use her techniques to make the coral grow fast around the base of the poles to hold them in place.

Abdul

We wouldn't need to rebuild the houses and buildings. We could just hoist them up onto the poles and then build walkways between all the different buildings.

Miriam

We could have ladders down from the buildings so that people could still have access to the sea for fishing.

Ali

What about some of the strong storms we get? Surely they will destroy our pole structures?

Abdul

We are good builders, Ali. It would take more than a hurricane to blow over any structures that we build.

Thobeela

These suggestions all sound great. I think we should suggest them to the people and, if they agree, start work on the project.

Ali

We have plenty of time, what's the rush?

Abdul

We don't really know how much time we have. I think it is best to begin work as soon as possible.

Ibrahim

There will still be some questions we need to work out. For example, how will we grow our food? Perhaps some of the people will suggest ways to answer these types of questions.

Ali

I'm not sure about all this. I think I'll just take my family and move over to an island that is much higher above sea level.

Thobeela

We can't make you work with us or stay here. But you will need to put the options to your family. Some of them may wish to stay and they will be most welcome.

Narrator

The chiefs go off to put the idea to their families and ask for any suggestions to help.

Scene 5

Narrator
The group is back at the Virtual Deck.

Miriam
So that's how we ended up here.

Thobeela
Yes. Others didn't take heed of the greenhouse gases, so our elders voted to build the structures. And here we stand today.

Abdul
That was really great. It was just like being there and being part of the whole process.

Ibrahim
Our ancestors were very intelligent. It is amazing to think that an idea thought of hundreds of years ago is the way we live today.

Miriam
I wonder what happened to Ali and his family? Did they go to live on Long Pine Island, and if so, what happened to that island?

Thobeela
I think we might need another virtual trip back in time to find out the answers to those questions.

Abdul
I think it's very sad, though. If people had been a bit more thoughtful, maybe we wouldn't have had to move up here.

Sand

Written by Stanley Ling

We are minute particles of sand,
Inert,
In the desert.

We appear
Motionless
In the burning heat of the day.

We appear
Peaceful
In the freezing cold of the night.

There are zillions of us,
Layered, tiered,
Covering the desert floor.

You may think we sleep
Soundly,
But you are very wrong.

We are chameleons,
Ever changing
Shades, shapes, hues, patterns.

We are hands on a clock,
Imperceptibly
Moving to a new position.

We are nomads,
Shifting,
Restless for new places.

We are blizzards
In frenzied fury,
Tempestuously whipping.

Raging,
Spinning,
Stinging.

Subsiding,
Retreating,
Retiring.

Relentlessly
Reshaping
The landscape.

readingsafari.com

Check out these Safari magazines, too!

Have your say -

e-mail your Safari Tour Guide at
tourguide@readingsafari.com

New	Reply	Reply All	Forward	Delete		Send & Receive

- Inbox
- Outbox
- Sent Mail
- Deleted
- Drafts

Subject: The Restless Earth

Now you have read this magazine, is there anything you feel strongly about? E-mail your point of view to the Safari Tour Guide.

Find some fun things to do!

Go to –
http://www.readingsafari.com

Safari Superstar

Name – Jock Vassilopoulos

Age – 16

Find out more about this Safari Superstar at

http://www.readingsafari.com